MW00902991

This book is dedicated to the future generations with hope they will demonstrate compassion and empathy towards animals.

A big thank you to all the rescues and activists who work tirelessly to give the dogs a second chance, and help advocate for animal welfare laws. These rescues and advocates give animals a voice.

Ichabod-Where is the Glory?

Written by Gayle Ellias
Illustrated by Eric Wein

Ichabod, a disabled Malamute, was one of many dogs on a truck intercepted by No Dogs Left Behind (NDLB). NDLB is an East Asia-based rescue founded by Jeff Beri. It consists of activists who save dogs from the dog meat trade (DMT), raise awareness, and advocate for the implementation of animal welfare laws. There are very few animal welfare laws in East Asia to protect animals from cruelty.

Studies show that children who are kind and empathic toward animals are less likely to commit aggressive acts toward people when they're older. The importance of teaching young children kindness and empathy is paramount in helping them understand that animals experience both physical and emotional feelings.

Across the world, far, far away...

Was a cold sickly dog about to have a great day.

Frightened, being taken away on a truck,
what I didn't know, was that I was in luck!

I was with many dogs, all of us scared.
I knew soon we'd be safe and happily spared.

The truck stopped in the rain,
the lights made me blind,
we were being rescued
by No Dogs Left Behind!

It was dark, cold, and the
night was sure scary...

I was magically saved by a man named Jeff Beri!

When I walked, my legs were not straight,
back hunched over, with a wobbly gait.

I was named Ichabod, meaning:
“Where is the glory?”
An Alaskan Malamute,
this is my story.

I got shots and food to help make me strong.
Kind people and kisses made me feel I belonged.

With my friends from the truck, together we played.
Until adopted, it's here that we stayed.

The sanctuary felt safe, and met all our needs,
but I wanted a family where I could be free.

I watched seasons change, as many months passed,
I hoped to be noticed-I wanted a home fast.

My mom watched me play while searching online,

the silly smile on my face told her I would be fine.

She ignored my wobble and odd looking knees,

it feels good to be loved despite what one sees.

Then one winter day
I was put in a crate.
Traveled by truck and by plane,
what would be my fate?

The plane trip was long, tiring and scary.
Someone opened my crate, who else but Jeff Beri!

My mom came to get me and gave me a hug.
I knew right away this was going to be love.

I reached my new home, this is where I will stay.
To my surprise were 5 dogs, all waiting to play!

Flashing my smile I'll never look back,
my fur-sibs and I are now the "6-Pack"

There's Ace and Ixy, Fanny and Zuri.
Hoobly and I will make the house furry.

I am safe to live in the US of A.

Memories of fear and pain slowly slip away.

Rules say right from wrong,
they are meant to protect.

These rules are called laws,
animals deserve much respect.

Humans should protect us
everywhere, worldwide.
They need to be kind,
this comes from inside.

Ichabod's Family

(Left to Right) Hoobly, Ixy, (front) Ace, Fanny, Gayle, Zuri, and Ichabod

Portrait

Artist: **Georgette Hancock**

Accolades

Ichabod, posing here with mom Gayle, is now part of a pack of six. He has no idea he is disabled, and truly lives life to the fullest!
SAVED
Alaskan Malamute Official Fan Club
CONGRATULATIONS to 'Ichabod' ALASKAN MALAMUTE OF THE YEAR 2021!!!!
See More
AMOFC
ALASKAN MALAMUTE OF THE YEAR 2021
Ichabod
ALLIANCE OF THERAPY DOGS
Pet Therapy Team
No Dogs Left Behind.

Author

Ichabod: "Where is the Glory?" is the first book written by Gayle Ellias. Gayle is an outpatient clinical social worker who works with children, adolescents, and adults. Gayle is passionate about spreading awareness of the DMT and Alaskan Malamute breed. Ichabod's humorous and fun-loving nature inspired her to write this story as he emanates immense happiness and joy, despite what he experienced. His love for life is contagious, and he shares this endearing quality with others. In November of 2021, Ichabod was certified as a therapy dog through the Alliance of Therapy Dogs. He visits disabled children at Friendship Circle and visited the survivors of the Oxford High School shooting. Ichabod exemplifies that one can find pleasure in life regardless of one's journey; tragedy does not define us.

Gayle Ellias & Ichabod

All proceeds of this book will be donated to **No Dogs Left Behind (NDLB)**

Ichabod and his "fursiblings" can be seen on Instagram: **IchabodNDLB**

Illustrations

Illustrated by

Eric Wein

Eric Wein, illustrator, has been drawing regularly since childhood. He holds a BA from Queens College (City University of New York), and for many years he studied drawing and painting under Charles Pasqualina, a well known portrait and oil painter. Eric paints a broad range of subjects, mostly in oil, but he also creates illustrations, drawn by hand, primarily using acrylics and other traditional methods. Some of his works can be seen on: fineartamerica.com and dailypaintworks.com

Additional Artwork by

Georgette Hancock

Georgette Hancock, is a self- taught artist. Her interest was sparked later in life when a colleague at a women's shelter bought her some paints. She explains that her teachers are the world of spirit guidance. She describes painting as her way of communicating her passion for life, joy and most of all, freedom. Georgette, mother of Jeff Beri, is a Holocaust survivor. She came to the US in 1956. She lives in Oregon with her DMT survivor, Pepper.

Ichabod
I AM A
THERAPY
DOG

Made in United States
Troutdale, OR
11/29/2023